Tom's Titanic

by Jenny Jinks and Davide Ortu

FRANKLIN WATTS
LONDON•SYDNEY

Tom's Titanic

Contents

Chapter 1

Biggest Ship in the World

Tom gazed at the *Titanic*. It was huge. Bigger than he had ever imagined. He had no idea how something that size could float. "I'll ask Uncle Max", he thought to himself. "He's sure to know."

Tom's Uncle Max was one of the ship's engineers. Tom couldn't wait to go and find him down in the engine rooms.

"Keep up, Tom!" His mum grabbed his hand and pulled him through the huge crowd which had gathered to watch the *Titanic* set sail on her first voyage. Tom loved ships, and thanks to Uncle Max, Tom and his mum were lucky enough to have tickets on the biggest and most unsinkable ship in the world. Times had been hard for Tom and his mum since Tom's father had died, but Uncle Max had promised to look after them, and now they were all sailing to America to start a new life. Tom couldn't wait.

"Tickets, please." A man looked at them sternly. Tom straightened his waistcoat nervously. His mum had insisted he wore his best clothes today.

"This door is for first class passengers," said the man. He pointed to a crowded door at the other end of the ship. "Your entrance is down there." Tom's mum looked embarrassed. Tom didn't understand why it mattered which door they went in. They were all going on the same ship, weren't they?

Once on board, Tom and his mum made their way through the maze of corridors to their cabin. It was tiny, and they had to share with other people. But Tom didn't mind. He wouldn't be spending much time in the cabin. He intended to go exploring. And he was going to start straight away.

"Don't go too far," Mum told him. "And don't disturb Uncle Max while he is working."

"Yeah, yeah, I know," Tom said. He smiled to himself as he ran out the door. He wanted to see as much of the ship as he could. But first, he was going down to the engine rooms. He couldn't wait to see his uncle and check out all the huge machinery.

But it wasn't long before Tom got lost. All the passages looked the same. Tom started to panic. What if he never found his uncle? The ship was so big. Tom felt he could easily be lost for days without ever finding his way back. Then he saw someone rushing along the corridor towards him. It was Uncle Max!

7

"Ah, at last! I've been looking for you. Your mum said you'd gone exploring," he said. "Come on, come with me." Uncle Max led Tom into a long corridor. It looked like it ran all the way from one end of the ship to the other.

"Where are we?" Tom asked.

"This is Scotland Road," Uncle Max replied. "It's how the crew move from one part of the ship to another. Now, hurry. I didn't want you to miss it."

"Miss what?" Tom asked as he hurried after his uncle.

They went down some steps and stopped in front of a huge metal door. Tom had never felt so excited. But nothing could have prepared him for what he was about to see.

The engine room was a hive of activity. Every piece of machinery must have been twice the size of Tom and his uncle put together. Cogs turned, pistons cranked, and hot steam puffed. Crewmen ran here and there, rushing up and down ladders and calling out orders as they prepared the ship to depart. It was the most amazing place Tom had ever seen.

"Are you ready?" Tom's uncle said.

"For what?" called Tom, just as a loud bell rang.

"Full steam ahead!" a voice shouted. Tom knew exactly what this must mean. The *Titanic* was off!

Chapter 2

The Accident

It didn't take Tom long to learn the passages and stairways that weaved around the ship. He found the best routes to sneak in and out of the upper decks without being spotted. He even made friends with some of the crew, who would sneak him treats from the first class dining room. The *Titanic* felt like his ship. He could go anywhere he liked.

There were lots of other children on the ship, and Tom quickly made friends with them. It was great fun playing hide and seek, and chase around the corridors, especially as Tom always won.

"Hey! How did you get there?" the others said when he suddenly appeared in the corridor ahead of them. Tom smiled to himself. It was his little secret.

But most of all, Tom loved to be down in the engine rooms. Passengers weren't really allowed down there, but that didn't stop Tom. He loved spending time with Uncle Max and his workmates, and learning how everything worked. Tom wanted to be an engineer on a huge ship one day, too.

Tom hated being cooped up in the tiny cabin at night, so he would stay out as late as possible, exploring more of the ship, or watching the stars from the top deck.

One night, even though it was very late, Tom didn't feel like sleeping, so he decided to visit Uncle Max instead. Tom had never been in the engine rooms this late. It wasn't nearly as noisy and busy as it was during the day, and Tom wondered where his Uncle Max was. He heard laughter in the next room. He peeked his head around the door.

Some of the men were sitting around, having a break and playing cards. One of them spotted Tom peering round the door.

"You back again?" he said cheerfully.

"Tom!" Uncle Max said. "Does your mother know you're here?"

"Can't I sit with you? Just for a little bit?'

"Not tonight, Tom, it's late," his uncle said.

Disappointed, Tom turned back towards the door. But as he ran to the other end of the room, his foot caught on something. He tripped and fell into a large machine. The handle hit him in the stomach and turned. At that moment there was a loud screech of scraping metal and the whole ship gave a sudden lurch. There was a shout, and crewmen ran towards him. Without thinking, Tom made a run for it.

Chapter 3

Big Trouble

Tom kept running, ducking left and right, up and up

staircases in case anyone was following him. He had

no idea where he was going. At last, he came to

a stop under the grand staircase, and hid behind

a plant. Nobody would think to look for him there.

Two men hurried past, talking seriously.

"Keep it quiet. We have to fix this, and quickly.
We don't want to start a panic," one muttered.

Panic surged through Tom. What had he done?
He had to go back. He had to tell someone
what he had done before he got into trouble,
or worse, he got his uncle into trouble. Uncle Max
would know what to do. He always knew how to
fix things.

Tom raced all the way back down to the engine
room. But before he even got inside he could hear
the commotion and panic echoing up the stairwell.
When Tom entered the engine room, everyone was
rushing around shouting. The floor was wet.
What was happening?

Tom looked for Uncle Max but he couldn't see him anywhere. He had no choice but to try to find someone to tell and to fix the problem.

Tom searched frantically for any of the engineers. The water on the floor was getting deeper. It already covered his shoes. Tom couldn't understand what was happening. Then he heard a shout behind him.

"Tom! What are you doing here?" It was Uncle Max. "You need to go."

"I'm sorry. Please don't be cross," Tom explained in a hurry. "I didn't meant to break anything! You have to fix it."

"What are you talking about?" Uncle Max asked, taking Tom by the shoulders. "This isn't your fault. Listen. The ship has hit an iceberg. You need to get your mum and get to the life boats. Do you understand what I'm saying?"

"But you can fix it. You can fix anything. This ship is unsinkable. Everyone says so," Tom said, confused.

"There's nothing anyone can do," Uncle Max said seriously. "Tom, the ship is sinking."

Chapter 4

The Imposible Happens

Tom couldn't belive what his uncle had said.

Surely it was impossible for the ship to sink.

"How can I help?" Tom asked.

"You know the ship as well as anyone,"
replied Uncle Max. "Go and get your mum, your
friends, anyone you can find. Take them up to the
lifeboat deck – you have to be quick. There aren't
enough lifeboats for everyone. Use the passages
I showed you. You have to make sure they get on
the boats, or they will all go down with the ship."

"What about you?' Tom asked. "Aren't you coming?"

"I have to stay here. I can make sure everyone has as much time as possible to get off."

"I can't leave you!" Tom cried.

"Don't worry about me. I'll get a boat later, once I've done all I can here. But you must get on a lifeboat. You have to promise me."

Tom hesitated. What if his uncle didn't get out in time? Already the water was rising faster and higher than he had ever thought possible. He nodded, and Uncle Max pushed him towards the door. "Hurry. There isn't much time. Go. Now!"

Tom ran. He flew back up the stairs and along the passages he knew so well. He burst into the cabin. His mum was sitting up, waiting for him. Gentle snores came from the other bunks. No one had any idea what was happening. Tom grasped his mum's hand.

"We have to go. Quickly," he said breathlessly.

"What are you doing? Why are you wet?" his mum asked, not moving. She was used to Tom being dramatic.

"No time to explain," he said, pulling her up. "Everybody. Wake up. Grab your life jackets and follow me. Now!"

Tom pulled his mother out of the door and the others followed. He hurried along the corridor, banging loudly on all the doors as he went.

"Everyone up. It's an emergency!" he shouted. But people didn't take any notice of him. They thought he was just playing another of his games.

"Can you keep it down. People are trying to sleep here," a grumpy man said, slamming the door in Tom's face. But Tom refused to give up.

He led the few people that would follow through the maze of secret passages. But even they began to doubt Tom.

"This is silly," one person started saying. "I'm going back to bed."

"Stay down here," Tom said. "The ship is sinking."

"Don't be ridiculous, this ship can't sink," the others said, turning to leave.

Then Tom saw something that made his blood run cold. Water was beginning to seep along the corridor. "Look!" he said, pointing, his hand trembling. "Now do you believe me? Hurry. We have to go." There was no time to lose. They raced up to the upper decks. Tom was surprised that all the lifeboats were still there. He had expected to find half of them already gone. But everybody was calm. Didn't they realise this was an emergency?

A member of the crew held out some life jackets, but nobody took them. They didn't think the ship could ever sink.

Tom was getting more and more frustrated. Uncle Max and the others were risking their lives down in the engine rooms to save these people, and none of them were doing anything about it. He had to make all of them hear the truth.

"Listen to me!" he shouted as loudly as he could, standing up on the railing. "The *Titanic* is sinking!" People looked at Tom and his little group in their life jackets with a mixture of concern and suspicion.

"Are you trying to start a panic?" a crewman hissed.

"I'm trying to save people's lives. We need to get off this ship or we're all going to end up at the bottom of the ocean," Tom said.

"Oh it's not that serious," the crewman said loudly so everyone could hear.

People seemed quite satisfied by this, and started wandering back inside, giving Tom very disapproving looks as they went. Tom didn't understand it. Why didn't anybody believe him?

Chapter 5

Into the Blackness

Just then the ship gave another sudden lurch. It was starting to tilt. Nobody could ignore what was happening any longer. The crew suddenly snapped into action. Tom helped as they hurriedly prepared the lifeboats and started helping people onto them.

"Women and children first," the crewman told the gathering crowd. Tom made sure his friends made it onto the first of the boats. His mum got a seat, too. Then it was time for the first boats to be lowered down into the sea.

"Tom, get in," his mum begged.

Tom hesitated. He wanted to help, like his uncle. There were still so many people below deck who had no idea what was happening. But he couldn't help them all. He was scared. What if there weren't enough boats for everyone?

"Tom, quick!" his mum said, beginning to panic as the lifeboat started lowering down the side of the ship. More and more people were clambering onto the lifeboats now. The crew were working quickly to help people. He looked down at his friends. They were safe. People were finally leaving. Tom took one last look back at the people still waiting on deck. He remembered the promise he had made to Uncle Max and jumped over the side, landing safely in the lifeboat.

Tom huddled up close to his mum as the lifeboat rowed away. Everywhere, people were crying, and screams and shouts echoed across the still water. From a distance, Tom could see that one end of the *Titanic* was already almost completely under water. It was sinking fast. Tom thought of all the people still on board and shuddered. Lifeboats packed with people were being lowered into the sea. Tom hoped that somehow his uncle had made it onto one.

27

The air was freezing, but that wasn't why Tom was shaking. Then his mum started humming. It was a song she had sung to him as a little boy. One by one, everyone else on the boat hummed along, too. Tom joined in as a tear rolled down his cheek.

Tom had no idea how long they had floated in the freezing water on the tiny boat. He didn't dare look back at the *Titanic*. Instead he stared up at the stars until everything went silent, and he knew that it was all over. The only noise now was the sobbing of the few survivors on the surrounding boats, and the splash of the oars as they rowed into the blackness.

Time passed so slowly. Tom was starting to wonder if they would float away into the night forever.

Just then, a light shone out across the water. It got closer and closer, bigger and brighter ... it was another ship!

Once on board, Tom didn't leave his mother's side for a moment. He searched the other faces for Uncle Max, but deep down he knew he wasn't there.
"I never want to set foot on another ship as long as I live," Tom's mum said. But Tom didn't agree. He was more determined than ever to become a ship's engineer. Uncle Max had stayed behind to save as many people as he could. He was a hero. And one day Tom hoped to be just like him.

Things to think about

1. What type of story is this? What is the main event?
2. Why do you think Tom is so happy at the start?
3. What does Tom learn about the ship? How does he have fun with the other children?
4. Why does Tom think he is to blame for the ship's damage?
5. How does Tom feel at the end of the story? Why does he want to be like his uncle? How would you feel?

Write it yourself

This story is based on a real event in history, but the characters are made up. Retell a key event in history by creating characters of your own to relive the moment. Plan your story before you begin to write it.

Start off with a story map:

• a beginning to introduce the characters and where and when your story is set (the setting);

• a problem which the main characters will need to fix in the story;

• an ending where the problems are resolved.

Get writing! When did your event take place? Think about how your characters are dressed and how they would speak. Describe the setting and atmosphere and give lots of real historical facts to your reader so they recognise the event.

Notes for parents and carers

Independent reading
The aim of independent reading is to read this book with ease. This series is designed to provide an opportunity for your child to read for pleasure and enjoyment. These notes are written for you to help your child make the most of this book.

About the book
Tom is so excited whe his uncle gets him a ticket for the Titanic. On board ship, Tom's uncle shows him the engine room and Tom learns all about how the ship works. Suddenly, disaster strikes and they have to abandon ship!

Before reading
Ask your child why they have selected this book. Look at the title and blurb together. What do they think it will be about? Do they think they will like it?

During reading
Encourage your child to read independently. If they get stuck on a longer word, remind them that they can find syllable chunks that can be sounded out from left to right. They can also read on in the sentence and think about what would make sense.

After reading
Support comprehension by talking about the story. What happened?
Then help your child think about the messages in the book that go beyond the story, using the questions on the page opposite. Give your child a chance to respond to the story, asking:
Did you enjoy the story and why? Who was your favourite character?
What was your favourite part? What did you expect to happen at the end?

Franklin Watts
First published in Great Britain in 2019
by The Watts Publishing Group

Copyright © The Watts Publishing Group 2019
All rights reserved.

Series Editors: Jackie Hamley and Melanie Palmer
Series Advisors: Dr Sue Bodman and Glen Franklin
Series Designer: Peter Scoulding

A CIP catalogue record for this book is
available from the British Library.

ISBN 978 1 4451 6515 8 (hbk)
ISBN 978 1 4451 6516 5 (pbk)
ISBN 978 1 4451 6945 3 (library ebook)

Printed in China

Franklin Watts
An imprint of
Hachette Children's Group
Part of The Watts Publishing Group
Carmelite House
50 Victoria Embankment
London EC4Y 0DZ

An Hachette UK Company
www.hachette.co.uk

www.franklinwatts.co.uk